OFFICIAL ANNUAL 2025

GET TO KNOW ...
JACK B. QUICK

> **PROFESSION:**
> RACE CAR DRIVER

> **FAVOURITE GADGET:**
> SPEEDOMETER

> **LIKES:**
> ROARING ENGINES, GOING FAST, GOING EVEN FASTER

> **DOESN'T LIKE:**
> FLAT TYRES, CHEATERS

Jack B. Quick loves to feel and hear the roar of his race car engine.

But sometimes he forgets he's not on a race track!

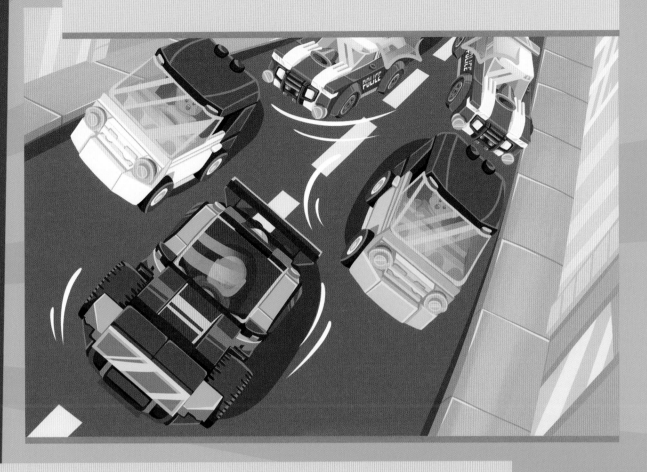

All Jack can think about is when he gets to race again.

Pit stop! Help get the car back in the race by writing the correct letters in the blanks.

A

B

C

D

E

These racers like to live life in the fast lane! Untangle the lines to match up the drivers to their vehicles.

A

B

C

Be fast or be last!

Help Just Jason get to his seat before the race starts.
Follow the flags in the order below to show him the way.

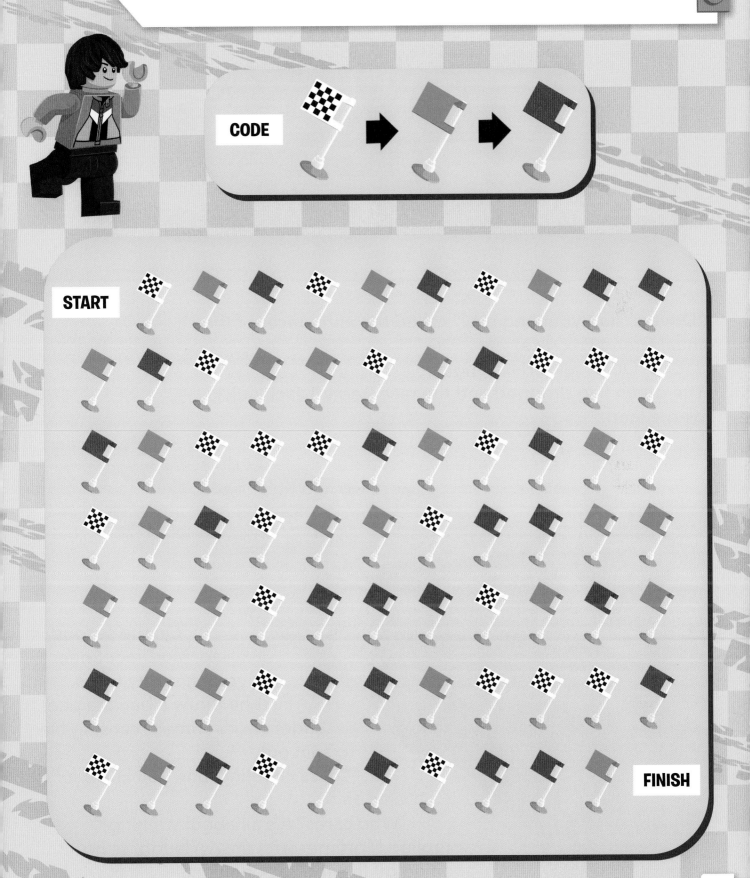

DIRTY TRICKS ON THE TRACK

"Drivers, start your engines!" called the announcer of the Annual Grand Prix race.

Jack B. Quick revved his engine.

The green flag dropped and the race began! Jack quickly took the lead.

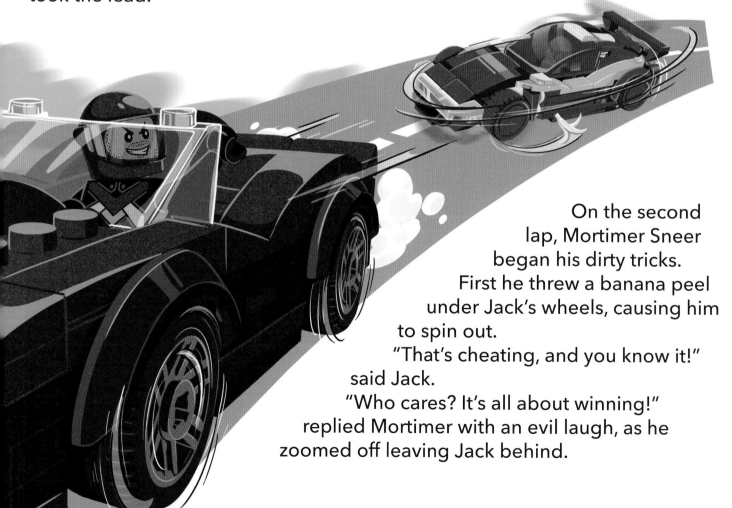

On the second lap, Mortimer Sneer began his dirty tricks.

First he threw a banana peel under Jack's wheels, causing him to spin out.

"That's cheating, and you know it!" said Jack.

"Who cares? It's all about winning!" replied Mortimer with an evil laugh, as he zoomed off leaving Jack behind.

Jack recovered and sped up to try to regain his top position in the race.
Suddenly he turned a corner and slammed on his brakes, his car stopping just inches away from a huge stop sign blocking the road.

"What's going on?" Jack asked his crew chief through the headset.

"Mortimer has barricaded the middle of the race track with a stop sign," said the crew chief.

"He can't do that!" said Jack.

"He does what he wants," said the crew chief. "And he wants to win so he can be on the cover of *Car Star* magazine."

Once the stop sign was removed, the racers zoomed off again. But it wasn't long before they encountered Mortimer's next trick: painting phony race lanes to divert the others off the track!

But Jack didn't fall for it. While Mortimer was busy making trouble, Jack was busy making history!

He won his 18th Grand Prix race. He thanked his crew and the fans. Jack smiled for the photographer of *Car Star* magazine.

"Mech Max here, and I've got news! Mortimer Sneer has been banned from racing for life, and can only ride tricycles from now on!" said the vlogger. "Mortimer, one question: what colour will your tricycle be?"

"No! No! Nooooo! This can't be true, it isn't fair!" shouted Mortimer.

To find out who won the chance to wave the checkered flag at the end of the race, choose the character that should appear in place of the question mark.

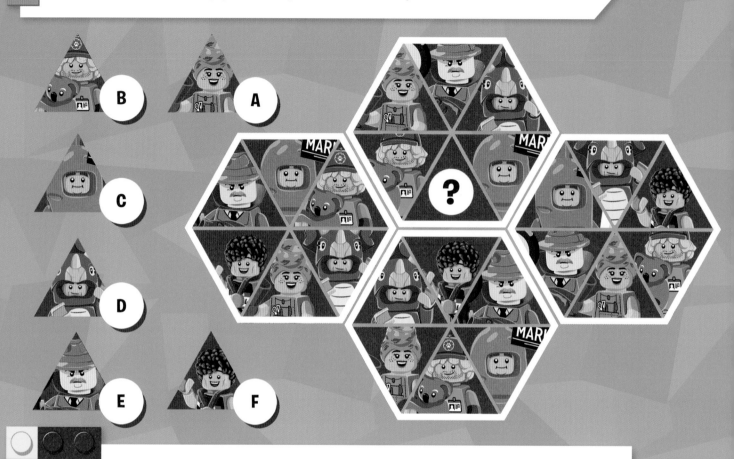

B A

C

D

E F

?

Practice makes perfect! Look at this Fitness Instructor and number her poses from 1–4, with 1 being the least detailed image and 4 being the one with the most detail.

On your marks, get set, go! Look at the close-up pictures below and match each one to the vehicle they are from.

I love the extra features these cars have!

13

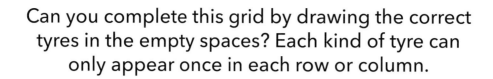

Can you complete this grid by drawing the correct tyres in the empty spaces? Each kind of tyre can only appear once in each row or column.

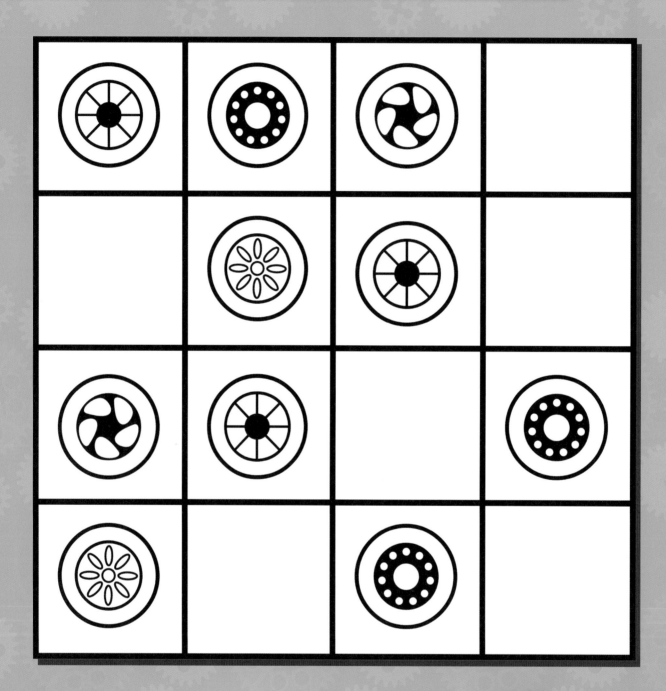

Who can guess what my favourite shape is?

This vehicle is lightning fast! Use the colour-coded dots to colour in the picture below and find out what it is.

Safety first! How many helmets are jumbled up below?

PARKING MASTER

Wait! Where's my race car? I parked it right here.

Now that I've got the wax to polish the cup, I can go home!

They've blocked my car in from every side!

Good thing I recently added some upgrades to my racer.

With the touch of a button I can turn on the propellers and just fly away!

Mech Max is gathering material for her channel.
As usual, she is most interested in monster trucks.
Find 10 differences between the pictures below.

Who is Jack's biggest fan? Read the clues and circle who it is.

The one you are looking for:

✓ Has a pet

✓ Has blonde hair

✓ Wears glasses

And the winner is ...? To find out who won the trophy, work out who appears in the grid three times only.

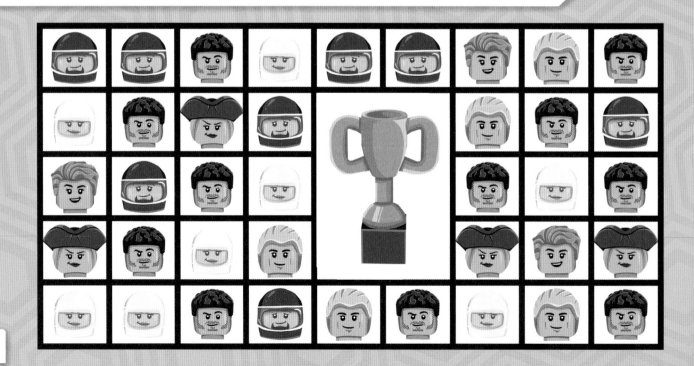

This monster truck goes full throttle! Compare the vehicle to the zoomed-in pictures and find the matching image from each set.

Watch out for that guacamole launcher!

The winner takes it all! Number the trophies from largest to smallest. The first number has been added in for you.

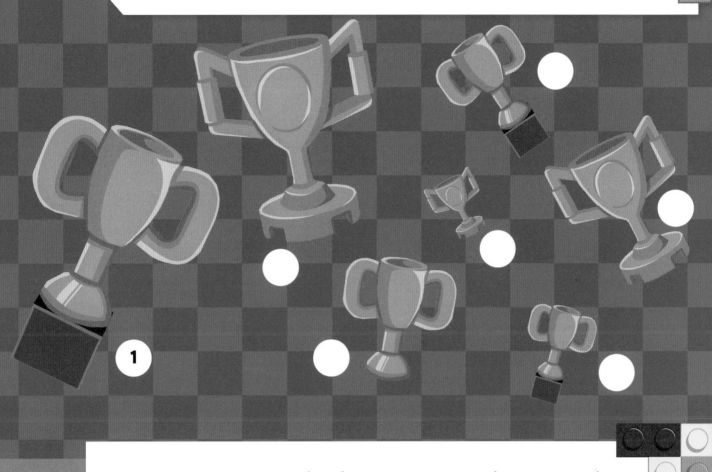

Construction work is happening near the race track. Circle the object that can't be found in any of the pictures.

Buckle up ... it's time to race! Complete the pattern by writing the correct number in the blank circle.

A B C D E

It's a blast to go this fast!

Yuck! Jack is covered in smoke from the racetrack.
Which is the clean version of him?

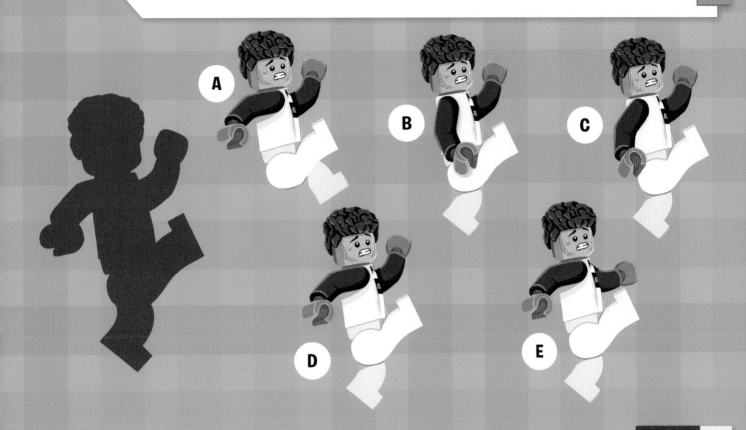

Jack loves watching sport. Number the pictures of
the race winner in the correct order. One number
has been added in for you.

This racing game is going to be loads of fun, but not until it's complete. Draw the missing parts of the digital race track.

Jack is off on another race. Find the path with the least cone obstacles to get to the trophy!

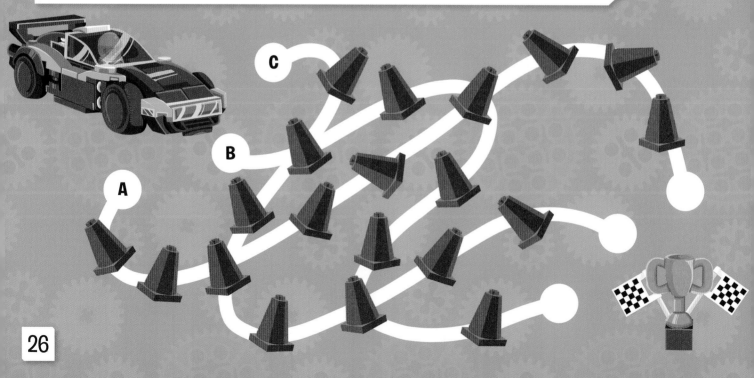

Time to put the pedal to the metal and get the go-kart to the finish line! Can you find the winning route?

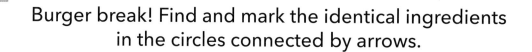

Burger break! Find and mark the identical ingredients in the circles connected by arrows.

Racing makes me so hungry!

Use the space below to design your own racetrack for Jack and his friends to race on. Make it as fun and crazy as you want!

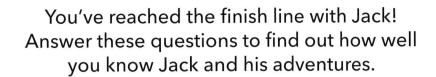

You've reached the finish line with Jack!
Answer these questions to find out how well
you know Jack and his adventures.

1. Jack's car is:

a)  b)  c)

2. What did Mortimer Sneer throw under Jack's wheels during the race?
a) Toothpick
b) Banana peel
c) Hat

3. How did Jack get out of the crowded parking lot at the car wash?
a) He flew away
b) He called the police
c) He left his car in the parking lot

4. What upgrade did Max add to Jack's car?
a) Coffee machine
b) Heated seat
c) Turbo boost

5. What cup did Jack win?

a)  b)  c)

You deserve the gold cup!

AIR

29

GET TO KNOW ...
RAPTON

PERSONALITY:
BOASTS AND BRAGS

SKILLS:
HUNTING DRAGONS

INTEREST:
COLLECTING UNICORN FIGURINES

GREATEST CHALLENGE:
PROVING HIMSELF TO PEOPLE WHO CALL HIM A FOOL

Rapton is the leader of the Imperium Claws. His mission is to capture dragons from across the Ninjago realm and bring them to Empress Beatrix in Imperium.

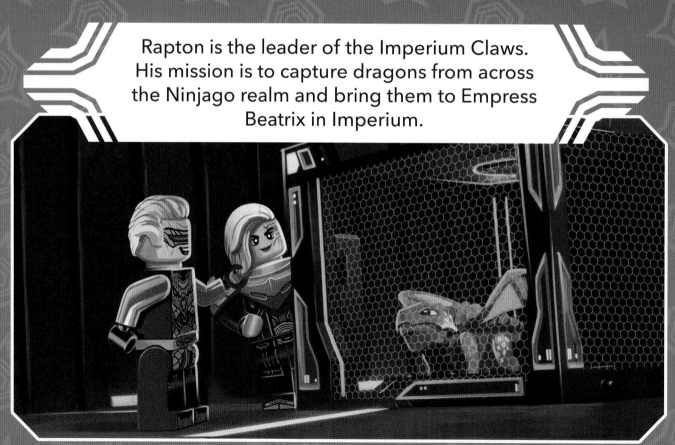

Rapton is very good at his job, but sometimes the ninja foil his plans.

He's to recapture those dragons and find more! Imperium is counting on him.

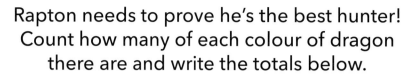

Rapton needs to prove he's the best hunter!
Count how many of each colour of dragon
there are and write the totals below.

I will show Lord Ras that I deserve the
Hunter of the Year Award!

Rapton's Hover Chariot is fast! Find 7 differences between these two chariots.

Rapton's secret passion is collecting unicorn figures! Use the colour-coded dots to reveal his favourite unicorn below.

Unicorns are hardcore!

I'll get rid of those pesky ninja once and for all! Follow the matching footprints to help Rapton track down Sora.

Now that I know where she is, I just need to find my way through this footprint maze.

All dragons must be captured! Number the dragons from smallest to largest. The first number has been added for you.

Beat a ninja on a mech? Rapton thinks it's a piece of cake! To find out who he will fight, follow the clues.

The mech Rapton will face ...
- has gold accessories
- is not on the top row
- has two katanas

RAPTON'S UNICORN

The Temple of the Dragon Cores is an incredible place.
Connect each set of coloured dots to see it all.

I heard that this temple is haunted …

Follow the colour code to discover which weapon Rapton will take with him on his dragon hunt today.

CODE

START

Empress Beatrix has a truly royal mech that has risen from her own throne. Find its shadow below.

A

B

C

D

Riyu the dragon has grown a lot recently! See for yourself and number the fragments in the correct order. One number has been added in for you.

1	2	3	4	5

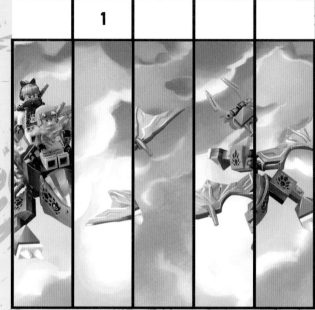

		1		

Guide Rapton through the maze to collect all the dragon paw prints. Choose a route so that he doesn't walk the same path twice.

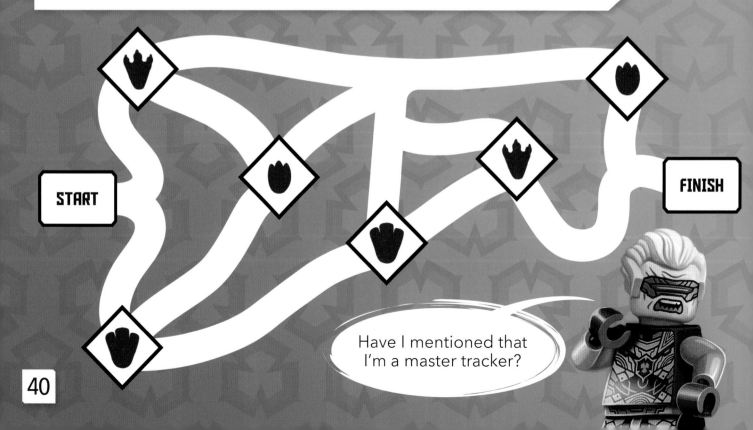

START

FINISH

Have I mentioned that I'm a master tracker?

Mark the picture fragments that appear in the big scene.

Rapton is following a path of prints to the Imperium Dragon Hunter Hound. Tick the path with the most prints.

I'm on my way!

Every day, Rapton looks in the mirror and makes sure he looks as fantastic as the day before. Find his mirror image.

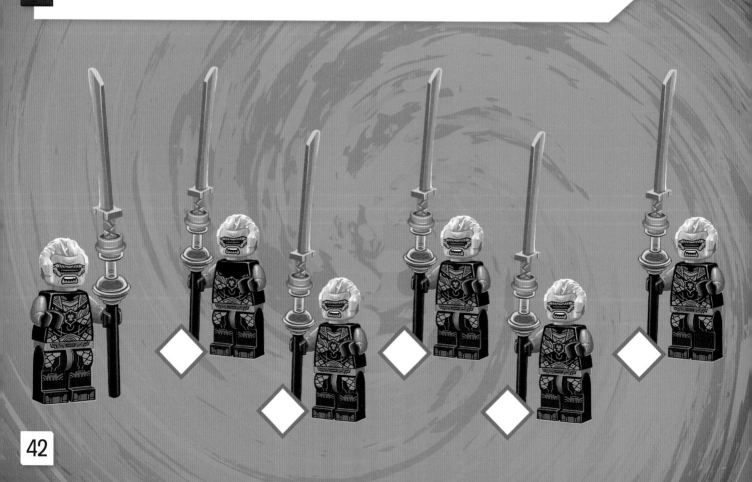

Rapton is gathering his team. Circle the missing character in each picture.

Oops! Raptor has forgotten the code to open the door to his room. Which pattern at the bottom of the page does he need to select to connect the elements and unlock the door?

Rapton is convinced he will one day be hailed as Imperial Hunter of the Year by Empress Beatrix. Draw the prize you imagine he dreams of.

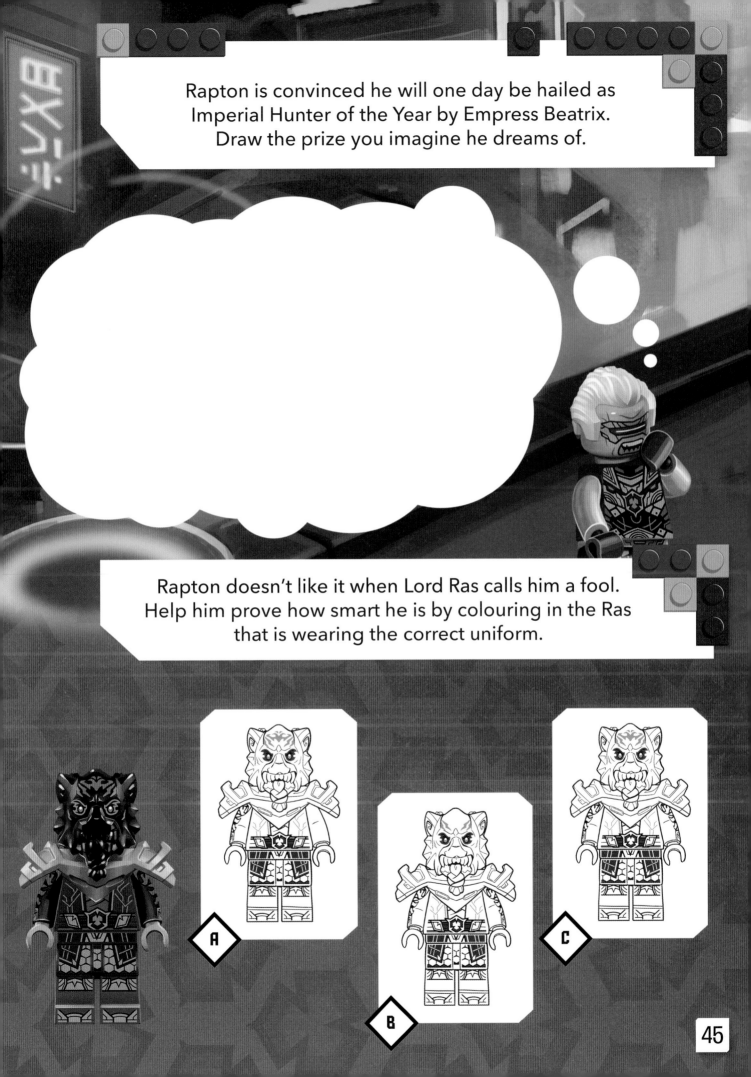

Rapton doesn't like it when Lord Ras calls him a fool. Help him prove how smart he is by colouring in the Ras that is wearing the correct uniform.

A

B

C

I'M NOT A FOOL!
BY STACIA DEUTSCH

Rapton hid in the bushes outside the ice cream parlour. Sora and Arin were inside.

Lord Ras always called him a "fool". Today, Rapton was going to prove, once and for all, that he was nobody's fool! He planned to follow the ninja, find out where they were keeping that pesky dragon Riyu, and bring that beast back to Empress Beatrix. He'd be a hero, praised for his genius. Lord Ras would call him whatever the opposite of "fool" was! "Un-fool". Or "non-fool"! This was going to be the best moment of Rapton's life!

It was uncomfortable in the bushes and he had to fight off ants and bees, but in the end, it paid off. When the ninja walked out of the shop, Sora said, "Let's get Riyu and take him to the forest for some exercise."

Arin responded, "That's a great idea. You know how he loves the meadow."

"The one with the purple flowers?" Sora said. "By the stream?"

"Exactly!" Arin cheered.

The two of them walked away, ice cream cones dripping in the hot summer sun.

Rapton hurried to the alley where he'd parked his Hover Chariot. He needed to take off immediately. When Sora and Arin arrived in the forest, he planned to already be there - he was going to ambush them!

"Riyu will be mine," Rapton chuckled, pulling back on the gear stick excitedly. The controller broke-off in his hand. "Oh no!" If he couldn't move his chariot, how was he going to get to the forest first?

Rapton took a deep breath and thought about the problem logically. He had time. Sora and Arin had to go to wherever they were hiding Riyu, get the dragon, then make their way to the forest. "I'll only be a little late," he told himself as he went to get a new controller.

After he fixed it, Rapton got back into the vehicle. The new gear stick worked. He zoomed towards the forest.

"Oh no!" Rapton exclaimed when he realized that he'd left his spear at the Imperium Palace. How was he going to capture Riyu without a weapon?

Rapton took another deep breath and again, thought about the problem logically.

Dragons needed a lot of exercise. Even if the ninja beat him to the forest meadow, they'd be there a while. Rapton turned his Hover Chariot and went to the palace instead. He parked, then rushed inside to grab his weapon.

Now ready to go, Rapton was about to head to the forest when Lord Ras called out, "Rapton! I've been looking for you." He waved a stack of papers. "You forgot to sign these official requests."

"Can I do it later?" Rapton asked, glancing frantically from Lord Ras to his Hover Chariot. "There's somewhere I need to be."

"What is more important than this paperwork?" Lord Ras asked.

Rapton blurted out, "I know where Riyu is. I am going to capture him."

Lord Ras said, "I'll come with you." But he didn't head toward his own vehicle. Instead he said, "Wait here. Empress Beatrix is going to want to come along as well."

"No—" Rapton began to protest, but Lord Ras hurried away.

When Lord Ras reappeared, the Empress was with him and so were a lot of other people. Was all of Imperium coming along, too?

"Great!" Rapton decided it was good to have witnesses to his success.

Off they went. Rapton's chariot led the others.

When they got to the forest, Rapton went straight to the meadow with the purple flowers. He checked the stream. The forest was quiet.

Rapton spotted an old man hiking in the woods. "You there!" he called out. "Have you seen two ninja and a dragon?"

"They left hours ago," the man replied. "They circled the forest 5,463 times and then returned to the temple."

"How could I be so late?" Rapton said. But then, he remembered all the things that had happened before he came to the forest.

"You're a fool," Lord Ras declared in front of everyone.

At first, Rapton frowned, but then he straightened his shoulders and declared, "Next time, I'll prove to everyone that I am the greatest UN-FOOL Imperium has ever seen. Just you wait!"

Dragon Hunters are going out in pairs. Match the identical codes to discover the teams.

Let's go get some dragons!

Rapton is adding to his collection. Separate these into four groups, so each group contains one of every type of unicorn. One group has been found for you.

Horns on their faces!

Who is Rapton fighting next? Find the missing piece so he can begin the duel.

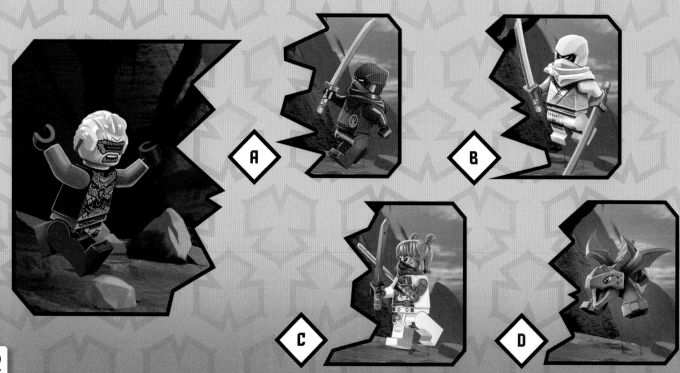

A

B

C

D

Rapton wants to take a closer look at Kai's new mech before the duel begins. Compare the large mech to the zoomed-in pictures and find the matching image from each set.

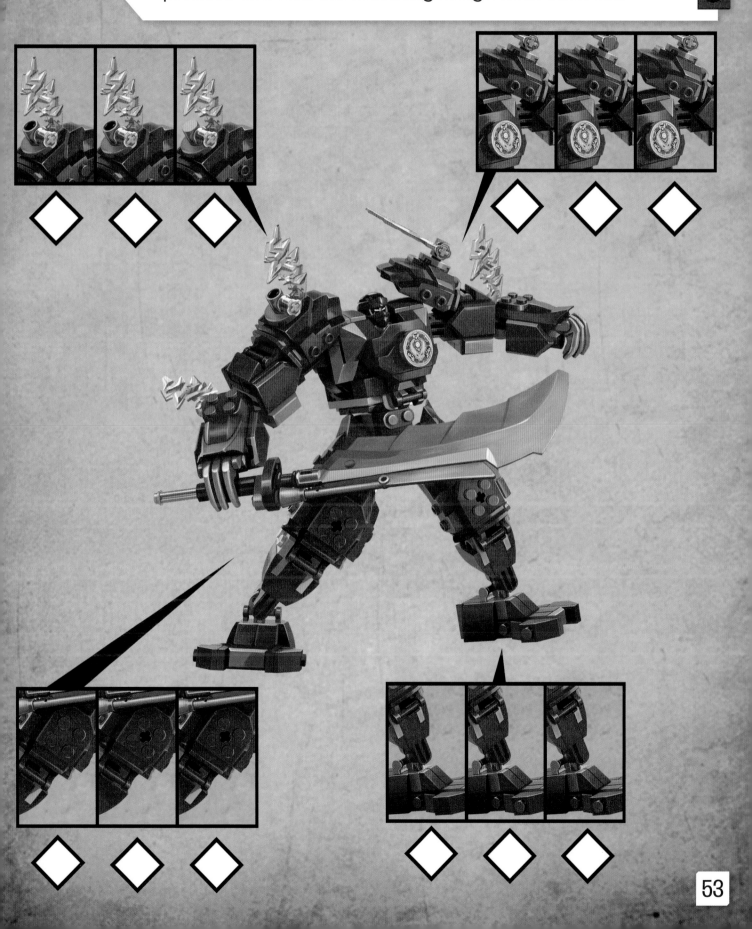

Rapton has lost his weapon. To help him find it, connect the lines in the empty boxes.

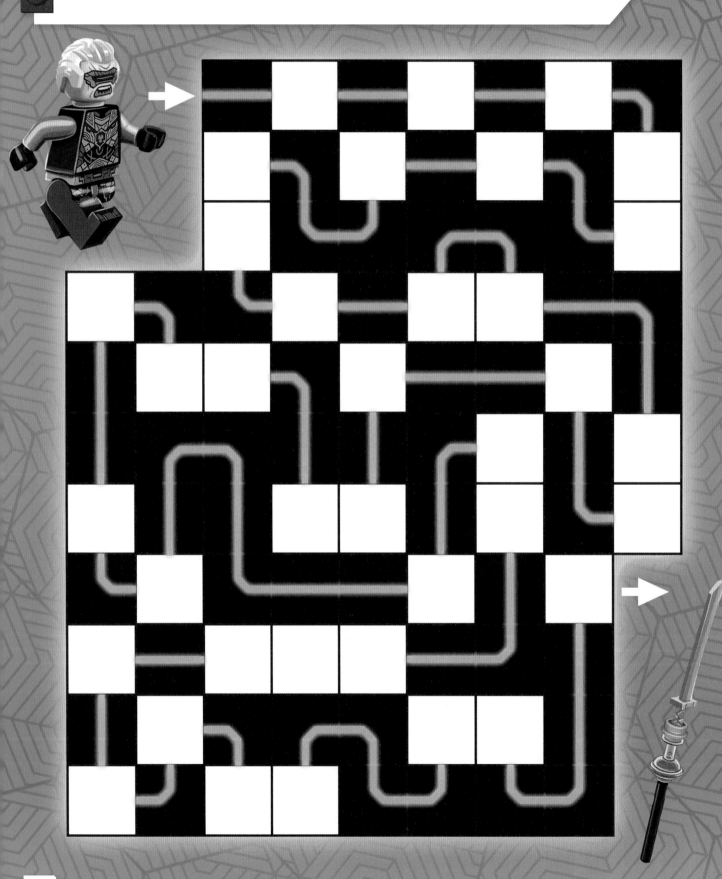

I AM RAPTON!

There's one thing different in each of these pictures. Compare the big picture of Rapton with each of the smaller ones below and find all of the differences.

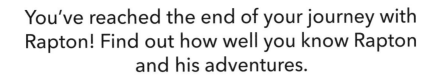

You've reached the end of your journey with Rapton! Find out how well you know Rapton and his adventures.

1. Rapton collects:

 a)   b)    c)

2. Rapton hates when someone:
   a) Sneezes loudly
   b) Forgets his name
   c) Talks too fast

3. What did Rapton want to find in the forest?
   a) Mushrooms
   b) The missing part for his chariot
   c) Riyu and his friends

4. Which weapon belongs to Rapton?

 a)    b)   c)

Good job!

5. Rapton didn't want to catch the dragon that destroyed ...
   a) the mech footprints that Rapton was tracking.
   b) a unicorn figurine from the limited collection.
   c) his dinner.

ANSWERS

p. 6

p. 7

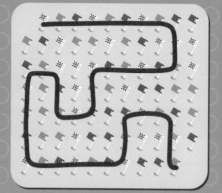

p. 12

p. 13

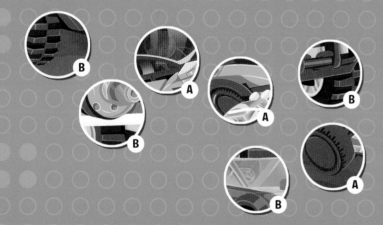

p. 14

p. 15

11

p. 17

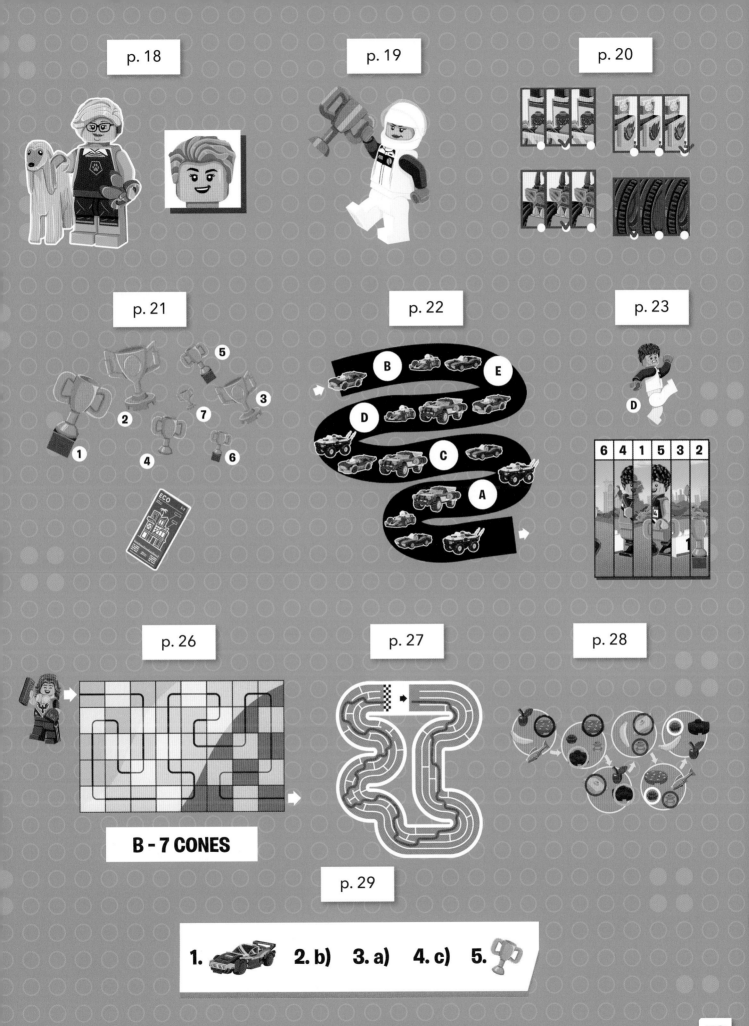

p. 18

p. 19

p. 20

p. 21

p. 22

p. 23

p. 26

B - 7 CONES

p. 27

p. 28

p. 29

1. 2. b) 3. a) 4. c) 5.

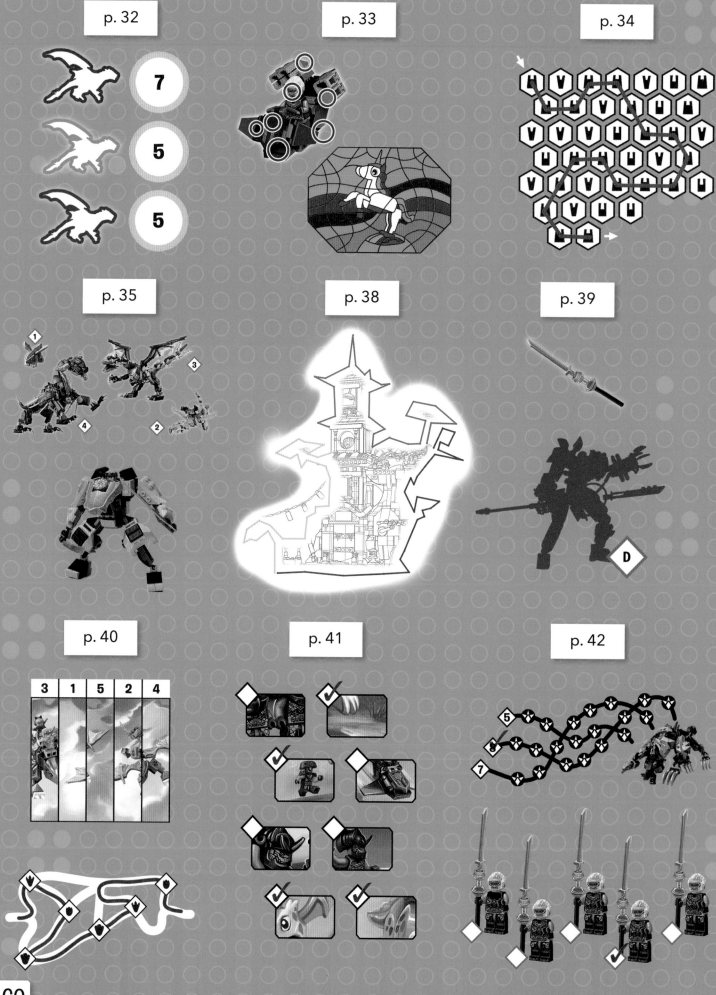

p. 32

7

5

5

p. 33

p. 34

p. 35

p. 38

p. 39

D

p. 40

3 1 5 2 4

p. 41

p. 42

5

7

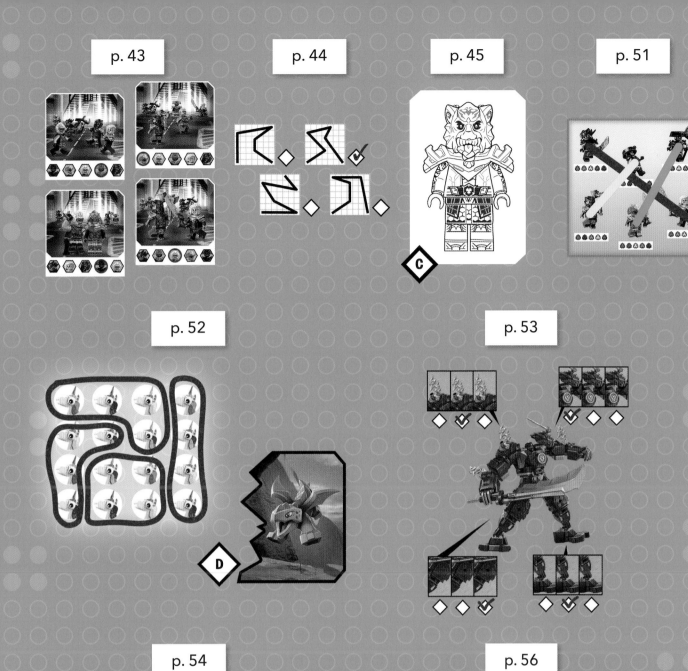

p. 43

p. 44

p. 45

C

p. 51

p. 52

D

p. 53

p. 54

p. 56

p. 57

1. 🦄 **2. b)** **3. c)** **4.** ⚔ **5. b)**

HOW TO BUILD JACK B. QUICK